W9-DDJ-803

Collections for Young Scholars™

READING/WRITING CONNECTION

VOLUME 1/BOOK 1

PROGRAM AUTHORS
Marilyn Jager Adams
Carl Bereiter
Jan Hirshberg
Valerie Anderson

CONSULTING AUTHORS
Michael Pressley
Marsha Roit
Iva Carruthers
Bill Pinkney

OPEN COURT PUBLISHING COMPANY

Cover art by Cat Bowman Smith
Interior art by Bob Barner, Normand Chartier, Nelle Davis, Linda Kelen, Hilary Knight,
Alexi Natchev, Cat Bowman Smith, Pat Traub, Jack Wallen, Nadine Bernard Westcott
Composition, electronic page makeup, and art management were provided by
Chestnut House Group, Inc.

OPEN COURT and ✻ are registered trademarks of Open Court Publishing Company.

COLLECTIONS FOR YOUNG SCHOLARS is a trademark
of Open Court Publishing Company.

Copyright © 1995 Open Court Publishing Company

All rights reserved for all countries. No part of this work may be reproduced or utilized in
any form or by any means, electronic or mechanical, including photocopying, recording, or
by any information storage or retrieval system, without the written permission of Open
Court Publishing Company unless such copying is expressly permitted by federal copyright
law.

Printed in the United States of America

ISBN 0-8126-1136-5

20 19 18

Sounds and Spellings

o

o_e

_oe

Writing Words and Sentences

doe _____

tiptoe _____

Joe hit his toe with a hoe.

_____

_____

Dictation and Spelling

_____ _____ _____

_____ _____ _____

_____ _____ _____

_____ _____ _____

_____

_____

_____

_____

Copyright © 1995 Open Court Publishing Company   Directions: Copy the words and the sentence on the spaces provided.

Name

Lesson 1

Games

Directions: After discussion, write or draw your feelings about games.

Copyright © 1995 Open Court Publishing Company

Name _____

Sounds and Spellings

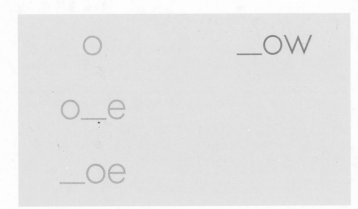

o   _ow

o_e

_oe

Directions: Copy the words and the sentence on the spaces provided.

Copyright © 1995 Open Court Publishing Company

Writing Words and Sentences

grow   _____   throw   _____

shadow   _____   yellow   _____

The snow blows slowly past the window.

_____

_____

_____

Vowel Sounds and Spellings

Directions: Finish each sentence with the appropriate word.

mumpity bumpity dumpity lumpity

miggle giggle wiggle jiggle

says	play	Piggle	game
Bear	sing	see	Homer

1. _____ wants to play with Bear.

2. "What shall we _____?" asked Bear.

3. Piggle is a _____ .

4. Homer and Bear play _____ .

5. They dance and _____ .

6. Homer talks to _____ .

7. Bear _____ , "Piggle like triggle."

8. Homer says, "Oh, I _____ ."

Copyright © 1995 Open Court Publishing Company

Sounds and Spellings

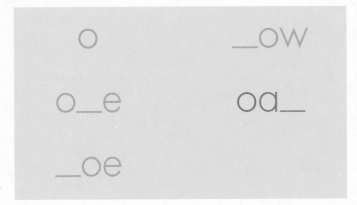

o   _ow

o__e   oa__

_oe

Writing Words and Sentences

soap _____

toast _____

A toad sat on the boat.

_____

_____

_____

Dictation and Spelling

_____ _____ _____

_____ _____ _____

_____ _____ _____

_____ _____ _____

_____

_____

_____

Directions: Copy the words and the sentence on the spaces provided.

Copyright © 1995 Open Court Publishing Company

Vowel Sounds and Spellings

"A Game Called Piggle"

R/WC 5

Reading and Writing

Directions: Read each rhyme, then read the sentences below. Order the sentences by writing the appropriate word on the space next to each sentence.

First	Second	Third

Jack and Jill went up the hill

To fetch a pail of water.

Jack fell down and broke his crown,

And Jill came tumbling after.

_____

_____ Jack fell down the hill.

_____ Jill fell down, too.

_____ Jack and Jill went to fetch water.

First	Next	Last

Little Miss Muffet sat on a tuffet

Eating her curds and whey.

Along came a spider and sat down beside her

And frightened Miss Muffet away.

_____

_____ A spider sat next to Miss Muffet.

_____ Miss Muffet ran away.

_____ Miss Muffet sat down to eat.

Copyright © 1995 Open Court Publishing Company

Name

Sounds and Spellings

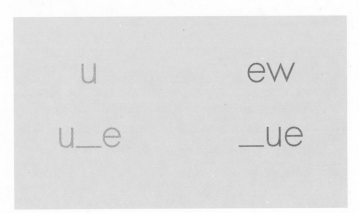

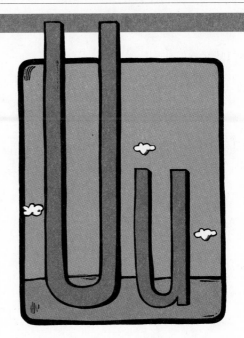

Writing Words and Sentences

few _____

pew _____

cue _____

hue _____

The fire fighter rescued the cat.

_____

Copyright © 1995 Open Court Publishing Company   Directions: Copy the words and the sentence on the spaces provided.

Name _____

Reading and Writing

| dance | long | nuzzle | tall |
| fast | jump | skip | strong |

Jafta likes to _____ like a spider,

_____ like an impala,

_____ like a zebra,

_____ like a rabbit.

Jafta can be as _____ as a rhino,

as _____ as a giraffe,

as _____ as a snake,

as _____ as a cheetah.

Reading the Selection

Jafta

Directions: Finish each sentence with the appropriate word.

Copyright © 1995 Open Court Publishing Company

Writing Sentences

1. What can you do like a deer?

_____

_____

2. What can you do like a snake?

_____

_____

3. What can you do like a tiger?

_____

_____

4. What can you do like a toad?

_____

_____

Dictation and Spelling

_____   _____   _____

_____   _____   _____

_____   _____   _____

_____

_____

_____

Directions: Read each question, then write an answer on the spaces provided.

Copyright © 1995 Open Court Publishing Company

Vowel Sounds and Spellings

Writing Sentences

Directions: Proofread, circle the mistakes in the paragraph, then rewrite it correctly.

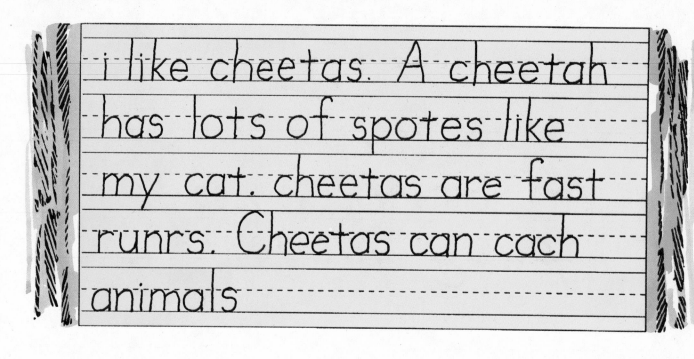

i like cheetas. A cheetah has lots of spotes like my cat. cheetas are fast runrs. Cheetas can cach animals

Copyright © 1995 Open Court Publishing Company

Jafta

Sounds and Spellings

Directions: On the top part of the page, copy the words and sentence in the spaces provided. Then write rhyming words to finish the sentences on the bottom of the page.

Writing Words and Sentences

how _____   down _____

_____   _____

Here is a towel for your shower.

_____

_____

_____

A cow that was <u>brown</u> went to the _____ .

The queen had a <u>crown</u> and a long green _____ .

I will plant a <u>flower</u> at the top of the _____ .

Copyright © 1995 Open Court Publishing Company

"The Big Team Relay Race"

Completing a Picture

The Race

Worm is winning the race. Cat is behind worm. Frog watches from the side of the road. Duck is in last place. The sun is high in the sky.

FINISH

Directions: Read the paragraph, then complete the picture with the information provided.

Using Story Clues

"The Big Team Relay Race"

Copyright © 1995 Open Court Publishing Company

Name

Sounds and Spellings

ow

ou___

Writing Words and Sentences

shout _____   house _____

_____   _____

The little mouse made a loud sound.

_____

_____

_____

Dictation and Spelling

_____   _____   _____

_____   _____   _____

_____   _____   _____

_____   _____   _____

_____

_____

_____

_____

Copyright © 1995 Open Court Publishing Company

Directions: Copy the words and the sentence on the spaces provided.

Vowel Sounds and Spellings

Directions: Finish each sentence with the appropriate word.

ran	team	Duck	first
Worm	fell	relay	

1. The animals ran in a _____ race.

2. Worm wanted to be on a _____.

3. _____ was Dog's stick.

4. The animals _____ with their sticks.

5. Dog gave his stick to _____.

6. Duck tripped and _____.

7. Worm crossed the finish line _____.

Copyright © 1995 Open Court Publishing Company

| how | sound | snow | crow | crown | show |

1. The queen has a _____ with a big round ruby.

2. Do you know _____ to play checkers?

3. The class put on a puppet _____ .

4. The balloon made a loud _____ when it popped.

5. The _____ made the ground white.

6. A _____ is a big, black bird.

_____
_____
_____
_____
_____

_____
_____
_____
_____
_____

Copyright © 1995 Open Court Publishing Company   Directions: Finish each sentence with the appropriate word, then list the /ow/ words and long o words in the appropriate column.

Vowel Sounds and Spellings

Quotation Marks

Directions: Find dialogue from "The Big Team Relay Race" and write it in the quotation marks next to the appropriate speaker tag. Also write the page number to show where the dialogue is from.

"All teams line up," said Owl.

" _____
_____
_____ "
_____ , yelled Dog.   page _____

" _____
_____
_____ "
_____ , said Worm.   page _____

" _____
_____
_____ "
_____ , yelled Duck.   page _____

" _____ "
_____ , said little Bird.   page _____

Using Dialogue

Copyright © 1995 Open Court Publishing Company

Reading and Writing

| outside | down | around | counts |
| shout | found | out | |

We play hide and seek _____ .

"Not It!" Rose and I _____ .

Steve is It. He _____ to ten. Rose hides under

the picnic table. I hide behind a tree. Steve hunts _____

the yard. I feel a tug _____ on my sneaker. It's my pup.

"Cut that _____ ," I say.

It's too late. Steve has _____ me. Now I'm It.

Dictation and Spelling

_____ _____ _____
_____ _____ _____
_____ _____ _____
_____
_____
_____

Copyright © 1995 Open Court Publishing Company

Directions: Finish each sentence with the appropriate word.

Vowel Sounds and Spellings

Name _____

Reading and Writing

| July | black | cents | high | Mack | back | fence | sky |

Directions: Finish each sentence with the appropriate rhyming word.

Miss Mary _____,

All dressed in _____,

With silver buttons all down her _____.

She asked her mother for fifty _____,

To watch the elephant jump over the _____.

He jumped so _____,

That he reached the _____,

And he didn't come back until the Fourth of _____.

Reading the Selection

"Mary Mack"

Copyright © 1995 Open Court Publishing Company

Reading and Writing

Mom and Kevin played Tic Tac Toe. Kevin made the board with nine squares. Mom chose X. Kevin chose O. Kevin made an O in the middle square. They kept making X's and O's. Kevin got three in a row.

"You win, Kevin," said Mom.

First	Second	Third	Last

_____ Kevin won!

_____ Mom chose X and Kevin chose O.

_____ Kevin made the game board.

_____ Kevin made an O in the middle.

Copyright © 1995 Open Court Publishing Company

Directions: Read the story, then order the sentences by writing the appropriate word on the space provided.

Story Order

Name

Reading and Writing

Directions: Read the first sentence in each group, then write the sentence that means almost the same thing.

1. **The crown was bright yellow.**
   The crown was big and heavy.
   The crown was shiny gold.

_____

_____

2. **Martha gave Mitch a present.**
   Martha gave Mitch a party.
   Martha gave Mitch a gift.

_____

_____

3. **Everybody looked at the clown.**
   Everybody watched the clown.
   Everybody liked the clown.

_____

_____

4. **Place the cup on the table.**
   Throw the cup at the table.
   Put the cup on the table.

_____

_____

Paraphrasing

Copyright © 1995 Open Court Publishing Company

Writing Words

Directions: Circle the compound word in each sentence, then write the two words that form the compound word.

1. The dog sleeps in the doghouse. _____ _____

2. The lightbulb is burned out. _____ _____

3. A stoplight is red. _____ _____

4. Mother has a new keychain. _____ _____

5. Jack played in the backyard. _____ _____

Dictation and Spelling

_____ _____ _____

_____ _____ _____

_____ _____ _____

_____ _____ _____

_____ _____ _____

Copyright © 1995 Open Court Publishing Company

Completing a Picture

Games

Megan plays with marbles. Jordan jumps rope. Mitch throws a ball at a basket.

Directions: Read the sentences, then use the information to finish the picture.

Copyright © 1995 Open Court Publishing Company

Using Story Clues

Writing Words

Copyright © 1995 Open Court Publishing Company   Directions: Add -er and -est to each word, writing the new words on the spaces provided.

tall

soft

big

wide

fast

thin

grouchy

brave

Making Comparisons

Completing Sentences

A _____ is bigger than a
_____
_____ .

mouse   cat

A _____ is smaller than a
_____
_____ .

dog   house

Sally is fast.

A _____ is faster.

A _____ is fastest.

car   dog

A rope is thin.

A _____ is thinner.

A _____ is thinnest.

shoelace   thread

Jon is tall.

A _____ is taller.

A _____ is tallest.

skyscraper   tree

A snake is long.

A _____ is longer.

A _____ is longest.

rope   road

Directions: Look at the words at the bottom of each box, then write the appropriate word to complete the sentences.

Copyright © 1995 Open Court Publishing Company

Making Comparisons

Matthew and Tilly

Name

Sounds and Spellings

aw

au

Writing Words and Sentences

straw _____   pause _____

The baby crawls on the lawn.

_____

_____

Dictation and Spelling

_____ _____ _____

_____ _____ _____

_____ _____ _____

_____ _____ _____

_____ _____ _____

_____ _____ _____

Copyright © 1995 Open Court Publishing Company

Directions: Copy the words and the sentence on the spaces provided.

Vowel Sounds and Spellings

Directions: Complete the paragraph with the appropriate words.

fight   yelled   sidewalk   friends   sorry

together   played   crayon   himself

Matthew and Tilly were _____. They

_____

_____ together all the time. One day, they had a

_____   _____

_____ because Matthew broke Tilly's _____.

_____

Tilly _____ at Matthew, and Matthew yelled at Tilly.

_____

Matthew went upstairs to play by _____. Tilly stayed

_____

on the _____ by herself. After a while, they were

_____   _____

_____. At the end they played _____

again.

Copyright © 1995 Open Court Publishing Company

Completing Sentences

1. The dog's _____ got dirty in the mud.

paws   walk

2. The cat's milk is in the _____ .

saw   saucer

3. _____ is the month after July.

Auto   August

4. Lightning _____ the forest fire.

called   caused

5. The _____ man juggled three _____ .

saw   tall   balls   shawl

6. The _____ has long _____ .

hall   hawk   chalk   claws

Copyright © 1995 Open Court Publishing Company

Directions: Finish each sentence with the appropriate word.

Games

Directions: Refer to page 2 and discuss what you wrote or drew. Then draw or write what you have learned.

Copyright © 1995 Open Court Publishing Company

Sounds and Spellings

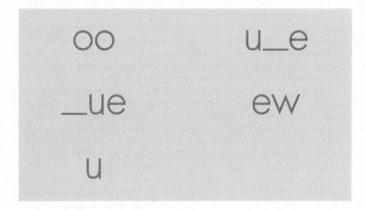

Writing Words and Sentences

food _____
_____

glue _____
_____

judo _____

flute _____
_____

jewel _____
_____

blue _____

The balloon floats up to the moon.

_____
_____
_____

Stu plays a new tune on his tuba.

_____
_____
_____
_____

Copyright © 1995 Open Court Publishing Company

Directions: Copy the words and the sentence on the spaces provided.

Vowel Sounds and Spellings

Name

Writing Words

Directions: Circle the long oo words in each sentence, then write the words on the spaces provided.

1. He huffed and he puffed and he blew the house down.

2. The farmer's goose honked at me.

3. I saw a cocoon on a leaf.

4. She made a house for bluebirds.

5. Do you know the rules of the game?

Dictation and Spelling

Vowel Sounds and Spellings

Folk Tales

Copyright © 1995 Open Court Publishing Company

Folk Tales

Copyright © 1995 Open Court Publishing Company Directions: Draw or write about folk tales you know.

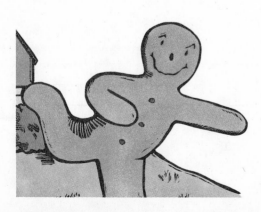

Sounds and Spellings

Directions: Copy the words and the sentence on the spaces provided.

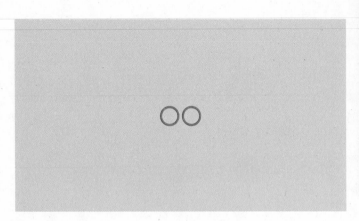

oo

Writing Words and Sentences

brook _____   hood _____

_____   _____

cook _____   wool

The woodpecker shook his foot.

_____

_____

She took a look at the book.

_____

_____

Vowel Sounds and Spellings

"The Gingerbread Man"

Copyright © 1995 Open Court Publishing Company

Paraphrasing

Directions: Read the first sentence in each group, then check the sentence that means almost the same thing. Answer the question at the bottom of the page.

Copyright © 1995 Open Court Publishing Company

An old woman wanted a child so she made one out of gingerbread.

____ An old woman wanted a son so she baked one.

____ An old woman wanted to make gingerbread cookies.

The gingerbread man hopped up and ran away.

____ The gingerbread man hoped to fly away.

____ The gingerbread man jumped up and ran.

Everyone chased the gingerbread man.

____ They all ran after the gingerbread man.

____ Everyone liked the gingerbread man.

The fox tricked the gingerbread man.

____ The fox tried to find the gingerbread man.

____ The fox fooled the gingerbread man.

What happened to the gingerbread man?

_____

_____

_____

_____

_____

_____

Sounds and Spellings

n

kn___

Writing Words and Sentences

knit _____   knot _____

The knight knocked on the door.

_____

_____

Dictation and Spelling

Directions: Copy the words and the sentence on the spaces provided.

Copyright © 1995 Open Court Publishing Company.

Reading and Writing

talking	again	stuck	burst	trouble
squeezed	bananas	threw	inside
fooled	Anansi	king	angry

Anansi _____ into a melon. He ate so much that

he got _____ . "I can trick Elephant," said Anansi.

"I will speak and he will think the melon is _____ ."

Elephant was _____ . He took the melon to show

the _____ . Anansi talked to the king from

_____ the melon. The king was _____ .

He _____ the melon and it _____ open.

Then Anansi hid in the _____ . "You got me

into _____ ," Elephant said to the melons. This time

_____ pretended to be a talking banana. He tricked

Elephant _____ .

Directions: Complete the story with the appropriate words.

Copyright © 1995 Open Court Publishing Company

Directions: Read the story, then list the long and short oo words in the appropriate column.

Brad Cooks

It was almost noon. Brad wanted to cook. He took out a cookbook. He used a big spoon to make the batter smooth. Then he put his cookies in the oven. Brad used a broom to sweep up his mess. He shook his apron. When the cookies were done, he let them cool.

_____   _____
_____   _____
_____   _____
_____   _____
_____   _____
_____   _____
_____   _____
_____   _____

Vowel Sounds and Spellings

Copyright © 1995 Open Court Publishing Company

Reading and Writing

1. Mama Bear is _____ than Baby Bear.

bigger   biggest

2. Papa Bear is the _____ bear of all.

bigger   biggest

3. Baby Bear has the _____ bowl.

little   littlest

4. Mama's chair is _____ than Papa's chair.

softer   softest

5. Papa Bear's porridge is _____ than Baby

hot   hotter

Bear's porridge.

Directions: Finish each sentence with the appropriate word.

Copyright © 1995 Open Court Publishing Company

Making Comparisons

Sounds and Spellings

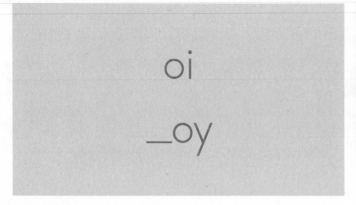

Directions: Copy the words and the sentence on the spaces provided.

Writing Words and Sentences

noise _____

_____

enjoy _____

The boy has a nice voice.

_____
_____

_____

Dictation and Spelling

_____ _____ _____
_____ _____ _____
_____ _____ _____
_____ _____ _____
_____ _____ _____
_____ _____ _____
_____ _____ _____

Vowel Sounds and Spellings

Anansi and the Talking Melon

Copyright © 1995 Open Court Publishing Company

Identifying Story Elements

Jenny wanted some flowers for Mother's Day. She went to the flower store. It was closed. On her way home Jenny found some nice flowers in a field. She picked them for her mother.

Who is the main character? _____

_____

What is the problem? _____

_____

How is the problem solved? _____

_____

_____

Copyright © 1995 Open Court Publishing Company   Directions: Read the paragraph, then answer the questions on the spaces provided.

Story Elements

Name

Reading and Writing

Directions: Circle the word in each sentence that does not belong; then write a word that could replace the circled word.

1. Dolls, yo-yos, and chickens are toys. _____

2. Noodles, crayons, and cookies are food. _____

3. Root, trunk, and hook are parts of a tree. _____

4. Five, foot, and elbow are body parts. _____

5. A goose, boot, and balloon can fly. _____

6. Oil, dimes, and pennies are coins. _____

7. Foil, boil, and bake are ways to cook. _____

8. A baboon, moose, and book are animals. _____

Vowel Sounds and Spellings

Folk Tales

Copyright © 1995 Open Court Publishing Company

Reading and Writing

Nick has to choose one toy. He likes the _____

_____ wagon. Nick also likes the _____ ball with the

_____ _____ stars on it. The toy Nick wants most is a

_____ bear. The bear has _____ fur and

a _____ smile. Which toy will Nick choose?

Copyright © 1995 Open Court Publishing Company   Directions: Complete the story by adding describing words; then illustrate the story.

Describing Words

Name

Writing Words and Sentences

gnaw _____   gnat _____

sign _____   design _____

The old tree was gnarled.

_____

_____

Stop at the sign.

_____

_____

Dictation and Spelling

_____   _____   _____

_____   _____   _____

_____   _____   _____

_____   _____   _____

_____   _____

_____

Consonant Sounds and Spellings

"The Lion and the Mouse"

Directions: Copy the words and the sentence on the spaces provided.

Copyright © 1995 Open Court Publishing Company

Reading and Writing

Copyright © 1995 Open Court Publishing Company

Directions: Complete the story with the appropriate words.

gnawed	lion	tummy	caught	little
help	free	learned		

Once a mouse ran across a lion's _____ .

The _____ grabbed the mouse. "Let me go and

someday I will _____ you," said the mouse.

The big lion didn't think the _____ mouse

could help him. Still, the lion let the mouse go _____ .

One day the lion got _____ in a hunter's rope.

The mouse _____ the rope until the lion was free. The

lion _____ that the little mouse could be a big help.

Reading the Selection

Reading and Writing

Directions: Finish each sentence with the appropriate word.

1. Jeff played with colored _____ .

mumbles

marbles

2. The _____ moved slowly.

turtle

rattle

3. _____ are hot and rainy.

Jingles

Jungles

4. The mouse _____ the lion's tummy.

tickled

tackled

5. Funny shows make me _____ .

grumble

chuckle

6. The green _____ was salty.

purple

pickle

Consonant Sounds and Spellings

"The Lion and the Mouse"

Copyright © 1995 Open Court Publishing Company

Writing

Copyright © 1995 Open Court Publishing Company

Directions: After discussion, use describing words to write about the picture.

Describing Words

Reading and Writing

Directions: Finish each sentence with the appropriate word.

1. The singer's voice was _____ .

loud
loudly

2. Ken's knapsack was _____ .

heavy
heavily

3. The dog gnawed the bone _____ .

noise
noisily

4. The fudge was _____ .

sweet
sweetly

Dictation and Spelling

_____ _____ _____

_____ _____ _____

_____ _____ _____

_____ _____ _____

_____

_____

_____

_____

Decoding/Spelling

"The Wolf in Sheep's Clothing"

Copyright © 1995 Open Court Publishing Company

Reading and Writing

"Let's make a house!" _____ _____ the mouse.

"Over there!" _____ _____ the bear.

"Next to the log," _____ _____ the dog.

"Near the thicket," _____ _____ the cricket.

"By the tree," _____ _____ the bee.

"Under the twig," _____ _____ the pig.

"I'll use my plow," _____ _____ the cow.

"I'll use my rake," _____ _____ the snake.

"I'll use my trowel," _____ _____ the owl.

"I'll make it flat," _____ _____ the cat.

"I'll rest then!" _____ the hen.

| roared |
| squeaked |
| purred |
| barked |
| hooted |
| clucked |
| mooed |
| chirped |
| hissed |
| buzzed |
| oinked |

Copyright © 1995 Open Court Publishing Company   Directions: Finish each sentence with the appropriate speaker tag.

Speaker Tags

Reading and Writing

Directions: Read the story, then list the /j/ and /g/ words in the appropriate column.

Gerry the Gardener

Gerry likes to work in the garden just behind her cottage. She grows many things like green beans and cabbage. She has the biggest carrots in town. Gerry likes to give her pals Ginger, Gail, and Jack the things she grows in her garden.

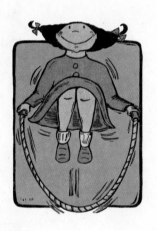

_____ _____

_____ _____

_____ _____

_____ _____

_____ _____

_____ _____

_____ _____

_____ _____

_____ _____

_____ _____

_____ _____

Consonant Sounds and Spellings

"The Wolf in Sheep's Clothing"

Copyright © 1995 Open Court Publishing Company

Reading and Writing

A wolf saw some _____ in a pen.

The wolf was _____ . He wanted

to _____ a sheep. The wolf

covered himself in a _____ . The

_____ pretended to be a sheep.

A _____ saw the wolf grab a

sheep. "_____" ! yelled the

shepherd. He _____ the wolf was

not a sheep. The wolf _____

like a sheep but _____ like a wolf.

Stop

hungry

shepherd

catch

acted

sheep

wolf

knew

looked

sheepskin

Copyright © 1995 Open Court Publishing Company

Directions: Finish each sentence with the appropriate word.

Reading the Selection

Sounds and Spellings

r

wr_

Writing Words and Sentences

wrist

wrap

A robot wrestles wriggly snakes.

Dictation and Spelling

Directions: Copy the words and the sentence on the spaces provided.

Copyright © 1995 Open Court Publishing Company

"The Three Billy Goats Gruff"

Reading and Writing

Wolf puppies learn to hunt by playing with each other. The puppies begin to hunt with the adult wolves when they are about six months old. When wolves gather to hunt, they say hello to each other by howling.

How do wolf puppies learn to hunt?

_____

_____

_____

_____

How old are wolves when they begin to hunt?

_____

_____

_____

_____

Why do wolves sometimes howl?

_____

_____

_____

_____

Copyright © 1995 Open Court Publishing Company   Directions: Read the paragraph, then answer the questions on the spaces provided.

Reading for Information

Name

Sounds and Spellings

Directions: Copy the words and the sentence on the spaces provided.

f
ph

Writing Words and Sentences

photo _____   gopher _____

phone _____   elephant _____

trophy _____   dolphin _____

Phil's nephew plays the saxophone.

_____

_____

_____

_____

Consonant Sounds and Spellings

"The Three Billy Goats Gruff"

Copyright © 1995 Open Court Publishing Company

Name

Identifying Story Elements

Directions: Write the answers to the questions on the spaces provided.

Who are the characters? _____

What is the problem? _____

How is the problem solved? _____

Copyright © 1995 Open Court Publishing Company

Story Elements

"The Three Billy Goats Gruff"

Reading and Writing

Directions: Circle the word in each sentence that does not belong, then write a word that could replace the circled word.

1. Squares, circles, and snakes are shapes.

2. Birds, children, and cats can sing.

3. Tennis, daisy, and soccer are sports.

4. Cars, rulers, and girls have feet.

5. Sandals, books, and sneakers are shoes.

Dictation and Spelling

Decoding/Spelling

"The Three Billy Goats Gruff"

Copyright © 1995 Open Court Publishing Company

Reading and Writing

Directions: Read the paragraph, then answer the questions on the spaces provided.

Copyright © 1995 Open Court Publishing Company

A billy goat is a male goat. A billy has long horns and a beard. A female goat is called a nanny. She has smaller horns and a shorter beard. Billy goats use their horns for fighting. Many goats live on high peaks. They can go up and down steep rocks.

What is a male goat called?

_____

_____

_____

_____

Why don't nanny goats look like billy goats?

_____

_____

_____

_____

Why can goats live on high peaks?

_____

_____

_____

_____

Reading for Information

"The Three Billy Goats Gruff"

Reading and Writing

1. The elephant was huge.

2. A plane was high in the sky.

3. Did Dad read the mail?

4. The day was cold.

5. Will Pat go to the store?

6. Pete has an ice cube.

7. The sheep are cute.

Directions: Circle the long vowel word in each sentence, then write the words in the correct columns.

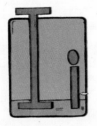

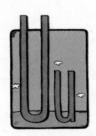

Vowel Sounds and Spellings

"Little Green Riding Hood"

Copyright © 1995 Open Court Publishing Company

Reading and Writing

potatoes	reading	Red	mixed
Yellow	giraffe	bad	grandpa

Directions: Complete the story with the appropriate words.

Copyright © 1995 Open Court Publishing Company

The child wants to hear the story of Little _____

Riding Hood. Her _____ tries to tell the story.

Grandpa gets the story all _____ up.

First, he calls the girl Little _____ Riding Hood.

Then he says that she has a sack of _____ .

Next he says that the little girl met a _____

in the wood.

The child thinks her grandpa is _____ at telling

stories. Grandpa will finish _____ his newspaper.

Reading the Selection

Reading and Writing

Directions: Circle the word in each sentence that does not belong, then write a new word to replace it.

1. Horses, chairs, and snakes have legs. _____

2. Robins, eagles, and lizards have feathers. _____

3. Bread, tubas, and sandwiches are food. _____

4. Phones, alarm clocks, and pigs can ring. _____

5. Ropes, buckets, and sneakers can be tied. _____

Dictation and Spelling

_____ _____ _____

_____ _____ _____

_____ _____ _____

_____

_____

_____

Decoding and Spelling

Copyright © 1995 Open Court Publishing Company

Reading and Writing

Did u read about the three
goats. It was a funy story.
The littl goat was cute. i liked
when the big goat bumped
the troll into the river.

Directions: Proofread, circle the mistakes in the paragraph, then rewrite it correctly.

Copyright © 1995 Open Court Publishing Company

Proofreading and Revising

Directions: Complete the story with the appropriate words.

smile	dress	spilled	spend	money	lay

A girl had a pail of milk to sell. She had the pail on her head.

As she was walking along, she began to plan.

"The man will give me _____ for this milk.

I will _____ the money for a hen. The hen will

_____ eggs. Then I can sell the eggs."

"Soon I will have money for a fine new _____.

Farmer Tom will smile at me. I will _____ right back

and nod my head, just like this."

When the girl nodded her head, the pail fell off. The milk

_____ on the ground.

What did the girl learn? _____

_____

_____

Copyright © 1995 Open Court Publishing Company

Folk Tales

Copyright © 1995 Open Court Publishing Company   Directions: Refer to page 31 and discuss what you drew or wrote about, then draw or write about what you have learned.